CHRISTMAS JAZZ

FOR CLARINET

ARRANGED BY JAMES RAE

FOR CLARINET AND PIANO
OR TRUMPET / TENOR SAXOPHONE

GRADES 3–4

www.**universal**edition.com

vienna · london · new york

UE 19 187

ISMN 979-0-008-03859-4
UPC 8-03452-04751-3
ISBN 978-3-7024-5481-4

CONTENTS

CHRISTMAS JAZZ

1

JINGLE BELLS

TRADITIONAL
ARR. JAMES RAE

Bright bounce tempo

SOLO

PIANO

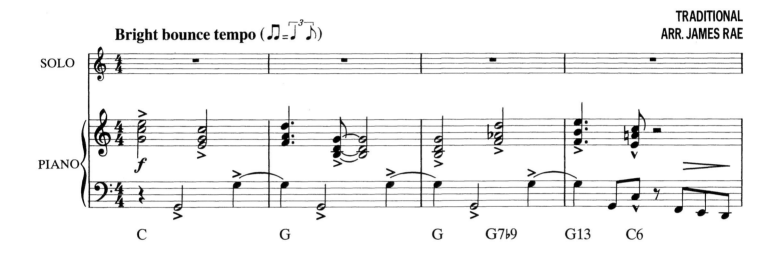

C   G   G   G7♭9   G13   C6

C   Dm7

G7   C

Universal Edition UE 19 187

GOOD KING WENCESLAS

TRADITIONAL
ARR. JAMES RAE

③

DING, DONG, MERRILY ON HIGH

TRADITIONAL
ARR. JAMES RAE

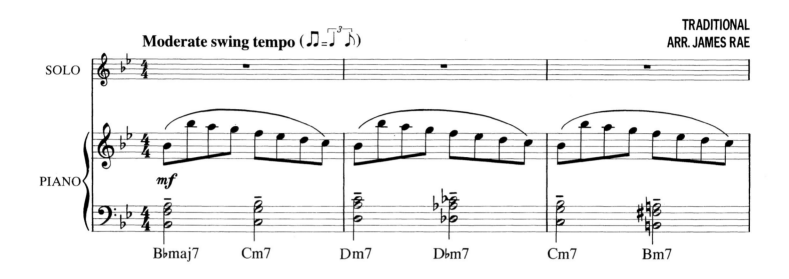

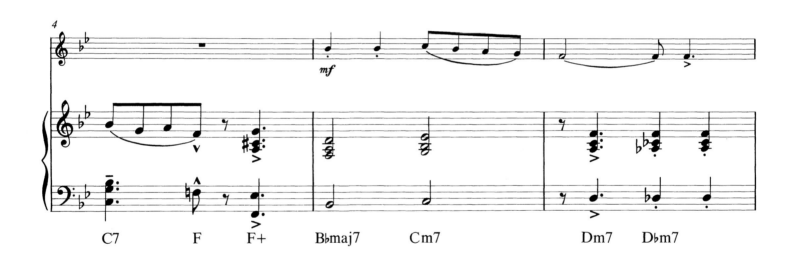

④

JOY TO THE WORLD

TRADITIONAL
ARR. JAMES RAE

CLARINET
OR TRUMPET
OR TENOR SAXOPHONE

CHRISTMAS JAZZ

1

JINGLE BELLS

TRADITIONAL
ARR. JAMES RAE

Universal Edition UE 19 187 a

②

GOOD KING WENCESLAS

TRADITIONAL
ARR. JAMES RAE

DING, DONG, MERRILY ON HIGH

**TRADITIONAL
ARR. JAMES RAE**

JOY TO THE WORLD

TRADITIONAL
ARR. JAMES RAE

5

O LITTLE TOWN OF BETHLEHEM

TRADITIONAL
ARR. JAMES RAE

Gentle Bossa Nova tempo (even ♪'s)

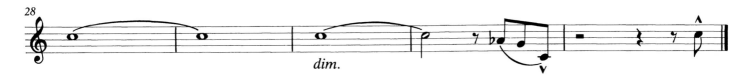

*May be played one octave lower if desired.

UE 19 187a

HARK, THE HERALD ANGELS SING

TRADITIONAL
ARR. JAMES RAE

GOD REST YE MERRY GENTLEMEN

TRADITIONAL
ARR. JAMES RAE

*May be played one octave higher if desired.

SEASON'S GREETINGS! A MEDLY:
Deck the Hall, The Holly and the Ivy *and* O Come All Ye Faithful

TRADITIONAL
ARR. JAMES RAE

*May be played one octave higher (to b. 47).

O LITTLE TOWN OF BETHLEHEM

TRADITIONAL
ARR. JAMES RAE

6

HARK, THE HERALD ANGELS SING

TRADITIONAL
ARR. JAMES RAE

Guitar: tacet

Guitar: Dm7   F   C13   F   F unison

GOD REST YE MERRY GENTLEMEN

TRADITIONAL
ARR. JAMES RAE

Guitar: tacet

Guitar: Cm

SEASON'S GREETINGS! A MEDLY:
Deck the Hall, The Holly and the Ivy *and* O Come All Ye Faithful

TRADITIONAL
ARR. JAMES RAE

Bright bounce tempo

Guitar: tacet

Guitar: G9

Cmaj7   Am7   D9   D13   G7

Guitar: tacet

Guitar: C13

Clarinet Albums and Tutors
in Lighter Styles

Easy

Introducing the Clarinet Plus Book 1 (clar. & pno) *James Rae*   UE 30 422

Easy to Intermediate

Introducing the Clarinet (Engl.) (clar. & CD) *James Rae*   UE18 780

James Rae's Methode für Klarinette (Dt.) (Klar. & CD) *James Rae*   UE 31 286

Introducing the Clarinet Plus Book 2 (clar. & pno) *James Rae*   UE 30 423

Introducing Clarinet – Duets (2 clar.) *James Rae*   UE 21 310

Introducing Clarinet – Trios (3 clar.) *James Rae*   UE 21 311

Introducing Clarinet – Quartets (4 clar.) *James Rae*   UE 21 312

Style Workout – Clarinet (clar.) *James Rae*   UE 21 301

Intermediate

Take Ten (clar. & pno) *arr. James Rae*   UE 19 736

Take Another Ten (clar. & pno) *arr. James Rae*   UE 21 169

Scott Joplin, 5 Rags (clar. & pno) *arr. James Rae*   UE 19 661

Jazz Zone – Clarinet (clar. & CD) *James Rae*   UE 21 031

Kurt Weill, 6 Pieces From The Threepenny Opera
(2 clar. & pno) *arr. James Rae*   UE 31 181

Kurt Weill, Music From The Threepenny Opera
(4 clar. or 3 clar. & bass clar.) *arr. James Rae*   UE 30 117

World Music Play-Along Clarinet (clar. & CD)

Klezmer *Yale Strom*   UE 31 569

Israel *arr. Timna Brauer & Elias Meiri*   UE 31 555

Argentina *Diego Collatti*   UE 31 566

Russia *arr. Ivan Malachovsky*   UE 31 557

Brazil *Jovino Santos Neto*   UE 31 562

Ireland *arr. Richard Graf*   UE 31 575

www.**u**niversal**e**dition.com
vienna · london · new york

723/IV 06